Foreword

by Andrew Blyth, EurIng,
RYA Yachtmaster O

Convenor of the ISO Worl
responsible for develor
international standard for the stab, ˌ …ˌ buoyancy
of small craft up to 24m length - ISO 12217

There are two fundamental requirements for all forms
of boats and yachts:
- they should FLOAT
- they should float with sufficient STABILITY to counter
  the hazards they may experience

In order to use a boat safely, people need to
understand:
- what makes a boat float
- what might make it sink
- what makes it stable
- what might make it capsize
- how to minimise the risks of sinking or capsizing
- how to recognise the operating conditions for which
  the boat is suitable

This book sets out to give users an appreciation of all
these factors, to help them to choose the right boat for
their needs and to use the boat safely.
A number of serious accidents could have been
avoided if the users had understood the principles
contained in this book.

A full understanding of the behaviour of sailing, rowing
and motor boats in a seaway is a challenging subject,
but the essential principles for safe operation are well
understood and are not difficult to grasp. Observing
these principles should avoid many unnecessary
accidents.

For those who would like to know more, a further
reading list is included.

Read, enjoy, and safe boating.

Contents

Introduction

Going afloat will always involve certain dangers. No amount of planning and preparation can make even the best design of boat 100 per cent safe. If it did, it would be a pretty dull sport. But sound seamanship and a good understanding of the environment and of the boat itself will reduce the risks and help the skipper and crew cope with potential hazards.

Although the RYA publishes over 60 books, covering every aspect of the sport from dinghy sailing to powerboat racing, none has concentrated specifically on boat design and how it affects safety. This book does just that. It examines the fundamentals of buoyancy and stability and applies these to offshore, inshore, coastal and inland craft both sail and power, big and small.

If you intend going afloat, in whatever type of boat or water, this book will give you basic knowledge of the principles of buoyancy and stability, the related hazards that you may encounter and lists the Do's and Don'ts of the subject. Although too small to be exhaustive, this book nevertheless gives sufficient information to enable skippers to gain a good understanding of why boats float or sink, stay upright or capsize.

Updated 2003

Stability and Buoyancy
Compiled by: Ken Kershaw I.Eng AMRINA, RYA Technical Manager
Technical Adviser: Andrew Blyth, EurIng, BSc, FRINA
Photo credits: Pete Goss OBE, Patrick Roach and PPL.

RYA

Published by
The Royal Yachting Association
RYA House   Ensign Way   Hamble   Southampton   SO31 4YA
Tel: 0845 345 0400   Fax: 0845 345 0329
Email: info@rya.org.uk   Web: www.rya.org.uk

A word about...

Design Categories

As of 16 June 1998 every new pleasure boat of between 2.5m and 24m length when first placed on the market must be CE marked to show compliance with the Recreational Craft Directive (RCD) which requires that a boat satisfies the Essential Safety Requirements according to one of four Design Categories. Design Categories are described primarily by the wave and wind conditions likely to be experienced and the circumstances under which such a boat might be used.

Design Category A - Ocean

Designed for extended voyages where conditions may exceed wind force 8 (Beaufort Scale) and significant wave heights of 4 metres and above, and for which vessels must be largely self-sufficient.

Design Category B - Offshore

Designed for offshore voyages where conditions up to, and including, wind force 8 and significant wave heights up to, and including, 4 metres may be experienced.

Design Category C - Inshore

Designed for voyages in coastal waters, large bays, estuaries, lakes and rivers where conditions up to, and including, wind force 6 and significant wave heights up to, and including, 2 metres may be experienced.

Design Category D - Sheltered Waters

Designed for voyages on small lakes, rivers, and canals where conditions up to, and including, wind force 4 and maximum wave heights up to, and including, 0.5 metres may be experienced.

So, if you are planning to buy or hire a boat, check which Design Category it has been given and whether or not this is suitable for your purposes. The Design Category and Manufacturer's Maximum Recommended Load will be marked on the builder's plate. The boat may also display an RYA stability label which confirms that the RYA has assessed the boat type against the ISO Stability and Buoyancy Standard.

ISO 12217 - Small Craft Stability and Buoyancy Assessment and Categorization

The Essential Safety Requirements of the RCD require (amongst other things) that a boat shall have stability, freeboard, and buoyancy characteristics appropriate to its Design Category. The RCD does not include detailed technical requirements, but relies on other, existing standards.

Because no universally accepted standard for assessing the stability and buoyancy of small craft was in existence, one has been developed under the auspices of the International Standards Organization (ISO). It attempts to classify all types of boats, whether propelled by sail, engine or human power, and to assign a suitable Design Category.

While other methods of assessing stability and buoyancy are permitted, ISO 12217, developed internationally, is rapidly becoming the preferred approach.

Buoyancy

Buoyancy is the force generated when a volume of water is displaced by a solid body.

Archimedes demonstrated that the mass of water displaced by a freely floating solid object exactly equals the mass of that object.

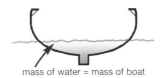

mass of water = mass of boat

Wood floats because it has a density less than that of water. The mass is less than the available buoyancy. A solid metal object sinks because it has a density greater than water. The mass exceeds the available buoyancy.

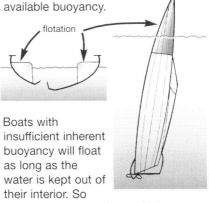

flotation

So, if the mass of a boat is less than the total volume of the material of a boat (its structure, ballast, engine and equipment) multiplied by the density of water it must always float, even if holed or completely filled with water.

Boats with insufficient inherent buoyancy will float as long as the water is kept out of their interior. So even an open steel boat will float provided it has sufficient underwater volume to support its mass and enough freeboard to keep out the water.

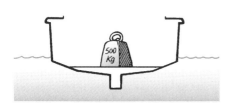

What are the buoyancy hazards?

The basic hazard related to buoyancy is that the boat might **SINK.**
Initially this always involves the boat filling with water because of:

- sudden swamping by waves, perhaps because of overloading or from the wash of another boat
- sudden swamping as a result of heeling to a large angle, perhaps because of an offset load or a strong wind
- slow swamping through submerged openings, hull damage or leaks through hull fittings

It will then sink if it:

- is not built of buoyant materials
- has insufficient flotation
- has leaky flotation tanks or water-sodden foam flotation

Stability

A boat is said to be stable if it tends to return to the upright position after being disturbed by external forces, such as waves, wind or movement of the crew.

The amount of energy trying to return the boat to the upright depends on three things:

- the mass of the boat

- the position of the centre of gravity **(CG)** of all the elements making up the boat and it's load (hull, masts, ballast, engines, fuel, stores, people, etc)

- the position of the centre of the volume of water displaced **(CB)** which depends on the shape of the immersed part of the hull. The **CB** will change with loading, heel angle and trim

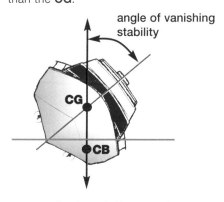

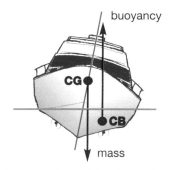

The boat is stable if, as it heels, the **CB** moves to one side more rapidly than the **CG**.

A boat may be stable when only heeled to small angles (say less than 30°) and unstable thereafter. The angle at which the boat will not return to the upright is called the:

Angle of Vanishing Stability

See Annex A: More About Stability.

What are the stability hazards?

A boat must have sufficient stability to resist the forces to which it will be subjected. If not it will **CAPSIZE**.

Causes of capsize include:

- excessive offset load, e.g. crowding of people on board, heavy weights on one side

- forces generated by waves, especially breaking waves

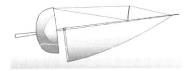

- strong winds
  (particularly applies to sailing boats)

- hydrodynamic effects
  (e.g. bad hull shape)

- reduction in the original stability
  (e.g. extra weight added high up the structure)

Hazards common to most boats

Bad loading

Overloading is a common cause of sinking or capsize, especially in smaller boats or those without decks. The amount of load that can be carried safely depends on the conditions and whether or not the boat is fitted with any form of flotation.

DO NOT OVERLOAD THE BOAT

Offset loading means that the stability is less in one direction of heel making the boat more vulnerable to swamping. It will have a list, even in calm water. If the offset load is too great, the boat may capsize.

POSITION THE LOAD TO KEEP THE BOAT UPRIGHT

Bad trim is caused by having the load too far forward or aft. Too far forward and the boat will be difficult to steer and will ship water over the bow. Too far aft and it will be difficult to turn and may ship water over the stern.

TRIM THE BOAT BY SHIFTING THE LOAD

Load too high reduces stability and makes capsize more likely. Putting the load low in the boat improves stability.

DON'T ADD LOAD HIGH UP IN THE BOAT

Filling with water

Swamping happens when an open boat or the cockpit of a decked boat rapidly fills with water from above. This may be the result of bad loading and/or wave action. Depending on the extent of swamping and whether or not flotation is fitted, a boat being swamped may sink very suddenly.

KEEP WATER OUT

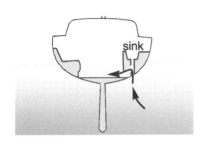

Flooding occurs when water gets into a boat more slowly, for example when relatively small openings are submerged perhaps intermittently. It may also happen because of leaky or damaged hull fittings and pipework, or via the toilet or sink.

CLOSE OPENINGS & SEACOCKS AT SEA

Reduction of stability

Extra topweight raises the overall **CG** of the boat and reduces stability. Fitting a radar antenna up the mast, or installing in-mast or headsail furling gear will inevitably reduce stability.

CHECK STABILITY IF ADDING TOPWEIGHT

Loose water inside a boat (or on deck) has the same effect as extra topweight. As the boat heels, the water rushes to the low side exaggerating the heel. This is called *free-surface effect*.

KEEP BILGES DRY AVOID WATER ACCUMULATING ON DECK

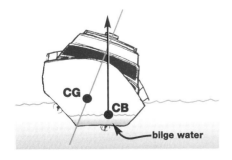

9

Hydrodynamic effects cause a reduction in the basic stability of some types of boat when travelling at high speed. This especially affects round bilge powerboats and broad, shallow draft monohull sailing boats.

KNOW YOUR BOAT AND ASK THE BUILDER

Resonant rolling

This occurs when an initial disturbance causes a rolling motion which is progressively magnified by the action of the wind or waves.

All monohulls can experience resonant rolling if encountering a series of fairly regular beam waves. The waves do not have to be especially large, but may simply have a period similar to the natural rolling period of the boat. Due to the damping effect of the sails, this is not normally of concern to sailing boats.

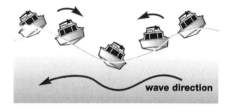

wave direction

CHANGE HEADING TO AVOID BEAM WAVES

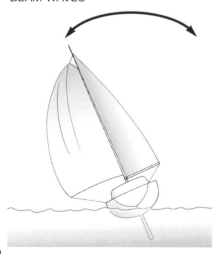

Monohull sailing boats running dead before the wind, even in smooth water, can develop a rolling action that can magnify so much that control is lost and the boat broaches violently.

SHEET IN THE MAINSAIL, OR RUN BY-THE-LEE WITH GYBE PREVENTER

Breaking waves

Waves are generated by the frictional effect of wind on the surface of the water. The stronger the wind, the longer it has blown and the greater the distance from shelter to windward (fetch), the bigger the waves.

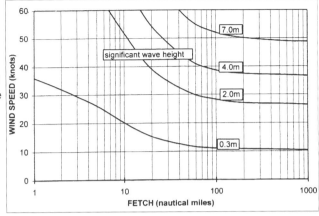

The graph shows what significant wave height to expect but waves will quite often be nearly twice the significant height.

Very steep waves are formed:
- when the wind strength is increasing rapidly
- when wind and current are opposed (wind against tide)
- when waves are coming from different directions (e.g. after a sudden wind shift)

Waves break when they reach a critical steepness and gravity can no longer sustain their shape.

Breaking waves release large amounts of energy relative to their size. In many cases* this wil be sufficient to knockdown and invert any boat under 24m length.

WHERE POSSIBLE AVOID LARGE* BREAKING WAVES
If unavoidable, do not take them beam-on, use a sea anchor if necessary.

* See Annex A for more information on breaking waves

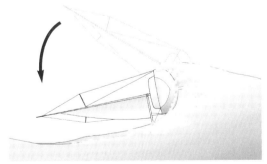

inversion often results

Broaching in following seas

This is the term used if, when running before large seas, a wave crest picks up the stern, causing the bow to dig in and the boat to slew through 90°.
The violence of this uncontrolled manoeuvre results in the boat being thrown onto its side, sometimes being completely inverted.
Traditional advice is to slow the boat by towing long loops of heavy warps or a strong drogue. An alert helmsman can often steer the boat away from threatening waves, but this is a tiring task and requires frequent changes of helmsman.

CHANGE HEADING

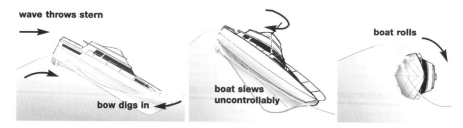

High speed handling

Fast boats, particularly powerboats and sailing multihulls, can experience various handling problems at high speed. These may result in dramatic swamping, sudden heeling, violent rolling, capsize or a combination of these.

KNOW YOUR CRAFT AND ASK THE BUILDER

Knockdown

All types of sailing boats may be knocked down, even in calm water, by a sudden strong gust of wind.
With many dayboats and dinghies this will lead to filling with water and possible sinking.
For most multihulls and some dayboats this will lead to complete capsize and inversion.

*BE ALERT IN GUSTY WEATHER,
AND BE READY TO RELEASE THE SHEETS VERY QUICKLY*

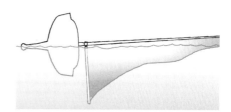

Characteristics of different boat types

Sailing dinghies and small catamarans

Most sailing dinghies and small catamarans will capsize, it's part of the fun. What is important is that they can be recovered.

Principal hazards are:
- Knockdown, leading to inversion
- Insufficient crew weight to right the boat
- Swamping, possibly leading to sinking
- Overloading, resulting in swamping, possibly leading to sinking

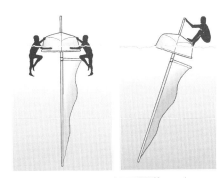

Look for and know:
- the minimum crew weight needed to recover after a knockdown or inversion
- the means of flotation when in a swamped condition. This should be located in the sides and toward the top of the hull
- the maximum number of crew for which swamped flotation is provided
- that, when swamped, the boat floats so that it can be bailed out by one person

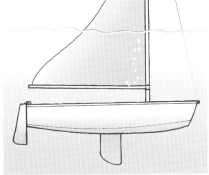

DO:
- ✔ be alert, and continuously shift your weight to counter-balance the wind
- ✔ make sure you know and practice the best way to recover after a capsize
- ✔ sail with enough crew to enable the boat to be righted
- ✔ have an appropriate size bailer attached by a lanyard
- ✔ check your flotation tanks or foam, in case they have taken on water, check that flotation bags are secure and fully inflated

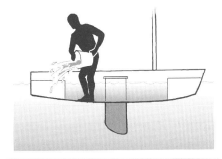

DON'T:
- ✗ carry more people than there is flotation for
- ✗ go out in conditions inappropriate for the design of boat

Sailing dayboats

Sailing dayboats may suffer from a knockdown and swamping but should recover without sinking.

Principal hazards are:
- Knockdown, leading to swamping and possible sinking
- Overloading, resulting in swamping and possible sinking

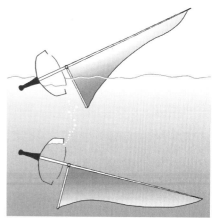

Look for and know:
- the means of reefing the mainsail
- the means of flotation when in a swamped condition. This should be located in the sides and towards the top of the hull
- the maximum number of crew for which swamped flotation is provided
- that, when swamped, the boat floats so that it can be bailed out by one person

flotation

DO:
✔ be alert, and keep the main sheet in your hand ready to release
✔ use crew weight to counter-balance the wind if necessary
✔ have an appropriate size pump or bailer attached by a lanyard
✔ check your flotation tanks or foam, in case they have taken on water, check that flotation bags are secure and fully inflated
✔ reef at the onset of rough weather

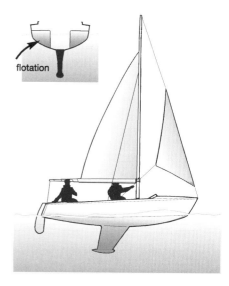

DON'T:
✗ carry more people than there is flotation for
✗ go out in conditions inappropriate for the design of boat

Offshore and coastal monohull sailing boats

Inversion for prolonged periods is a major hazard. A good design should avoid this.

Principal hazards are:
- Immersion of openings at large heel angles resulting in loose water inside the boat
- Knockdown by a gust, leading to swamping
- Resonant rolling, leading to broaching
- Breaking waves leading to knockdown or inversion
- Broaching in following seas
- Reduction of stability due to extra topweight e.g. radar, roller furling sails

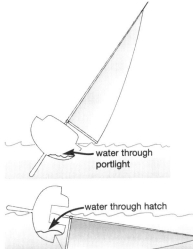

water through portlight

water through hatch

Look for and know:
- that all main hatches are near the centreline and that these and other openings can be closed effectively
- that the cockpit will drain overboard quickly
- the maximum steady heel angle to avoid downflooding in gusts (See Annex B for details)
- that the Angle of Vanishing Stability is ideally more than about:

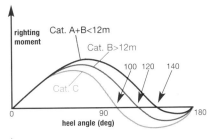

	over 12m loa	under 12m loa
Category C	95°	105°
Category B	120°	130°
Category A	130°	140°

- that the area under the positive part of the righting moment curve* is greater than the area under the negative part by a factor of about:

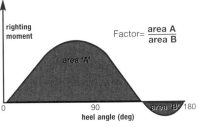

$$\text{Factor} = \frac{\text{area A}}{\text{area B}}$$

	over 12m loa	under 12m loa
Category C	1.25	2
Category B	4	6
Category A	6	8

- that extra topweight and additions aloft are included in the stability calculations

see Annex A for more information on righting moment curves

15

The following features will generally improve the ultimate stability of offshore and coastal monohull sailing boats:

- increased physical length
- heavy displacement for size
- high ballast ratio (upwards of 35%)
- high angle of vanishing stability
- high ratio of positive to negative areas under righting moment curve
- good righting moment at 90° heel
- modest beam in relation to length

- good but not excessive freeboard
- minimal topside flare
- absence of large nearly flat areas of deck
- large heel angle before downflooding occurs
- increased keel profile area
- absence of bulwarks

In developing the ISO Standard for Stability and Buoyancy, the ISO committee has agreed a formula for taking into account many of the above and other aspects affecting the stability properties of these types of boats. These include displacement in relation to length, topside flare, beam, downflooding angle and the wind speed at which downflooding is calculated to begin. This formula is known as STIX (stability index). STIX is based on previous work undertaken by the Royal Ocean Racing Club on Triple S, which was developed by the RYA as STOPS and is currently in used by the MCA Code of Practice for Small Commercial Vessels. STIX has been validated against a database of over fifty well known designs from six different countries.

DO:

✔ close hatches and other openings at the onset of rough weather

✔ check for water inside and pump out if necessary, before and during a passage

✔ be alert in gusty wind conditions, and reef before leaving sheltered water

✔ heave to, or run off streaming warps or drogue in extreme conditions, to avoid being caught beam on to waves

✔ ensure hatch wash boards will not fall out or be lost if boat is knocked down or inverted

✔ ask the builder for stability information, including a righting moment curve

Look for the following minimum STIX values:

Design Category	A	B	C	D
Minimum STIX	32	23	14	5

DON'T:

✗ in rough weather deliberately sail through known tidal rips, overfalls or areas where the bottom shoals rapidly

Offshore and coastal multihull sailing boats

Most large multihull sailing boats will not right after a capsize so it is imperative to avoid this.

Principal hazards are:

- Knockdown by a gust leading to very rapid inversion
- Sudden heeling after turning from a following wind onto a reach, caused by the rapid increase in apparent wind strength, leading to very rapid inversion

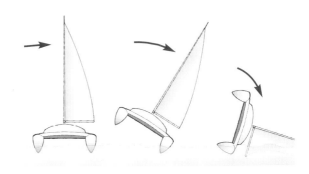

- Cartwheeling about the lee bow if pressed too hard on a reach leading to very rapid inversion

- Pitchpoling through carrying too much sail on a run leading to very rapid inversion
- Sinking after inversion due to overloading or failure of flotation

Look for and know:

- the builder's information on what sail to set in different wind strengths
- that the cockpit will drain overboard quickly
- how to escape from inside the boat after an inversion

DO:

✔ know at what wind strength you should first reef

✔ be alert in gusty wind conditions, and reef before leaving sheltered water

✔ know how to release the sheets quickly

✔ close hatches and other openings at the onset of rough weather

✔ check for water inside and pump out if necessary, before and during a passage

---

DON'T:

✗ forget that the apparent wind will increase sharply when turning from a run to a reach

✗ in rough weather deliberately sail through known tidal rips, overfalls or areas where the bottom shoals rapidly

✗ drive the boat hard when reaching or running, for fear of cartwheeling pitchpoling

Runabouts, open launches and dinghies

Also see the section on high speed powerboats if appropriate

Principal hazards are:

- Swamping as a result of bad loading, going too fast in waves or another boat's wash leading to possible sinking
- Capsizing as a result of loose water in the boat or bad load distribution, including passengers, causing excessive heel

Look for and know:

- the maximum number of people for which the boat is suitable
- the maximum recommended engine power as given in the owner's manual

either

- that the boat has good initial stability, is heavy and has a high freeboard

or

- has sufficient flotation fitted to stay afloat in a swamped condition. This should be located in the sides and toward the top of the hull

and

- the maximum number of crew for which swamped flotation is provided
- that, when swamped, the boat floats so that it can be bailed out by one person*

* ISO 12217 only requires minimal flotation to be fitted in non-sailing boats between 4.8m and 6m in length. A boat built down to this minimum would, if swamped, be impossible to bail out.

DO:

✔ bail out the boat before use

✔ take care to load the boat properly

✔ carry less load when it is rough

✔ check your flotation tanks or foam, in case they have taken on water, check that flotation bags are secure and fully inflated

✔ have an appropriate size pump or bailer attached by a lanyard

DON'T:

✗ overload the boat

✗ go out in conditions inappropriate for the design of boat

✗ go too fast astern, or astern into waves

Offshore and coastal cabin motor boats

Also see the section on high speed power boats if appropriate

Principal hazards are:

- Immersion of openings at large heel angles resulting in loose water inside the boat
- Resonant rolling in beam seas, leading to capsize
- Broaching in following seas
- Knockdown by breaking waves, causing damage to windows and superstructure, and sometimes to inversion
- Reduction of stability due to extra topweight e.g. radar

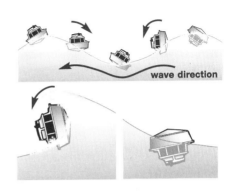

wave direction

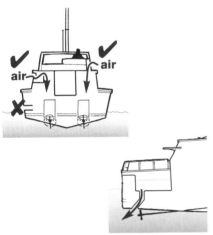

Look for and know:

- that hatches and other openings can be closed effectively
- that the cockpit will drain overboard quickly
- that the engine air inlet position is as high as practical and fitted with water baffles or traps
- the location of storm shutters for large windows (offshore only)
- that all additions aloft are included in the stability calculations

DO:

✔ close hatches and other openings at the onset of rough weather
✔ check for water inside and pump out if necessary, before and during a passage
✔ ensure hatches and doors can be strongly secured
✔ secure deck gear and dinghies when going offshore
✔ fit storm covers over large windows at the onset of rough weather offshore
✔ heave to, or run off streaming warps or drogue in extreme conditions, to avoid being caught beam on to waves
✔ ask the builder for stability information, including a righting moment curve

DON'T:

✗ in rough weather deliberately go through known tidal rips, overfalls or areas where the bottom shoals rapidly
✗ get caught beam-on to breaking waves

High speed power boats

Also read the appropriate sections on powerboats

Principal hazards are:

- Porpoising, the boat pitches continuously (even in calm water), sometimes quite violently

- Chine-walking, above a certain speed the boat either sits on one chine or oscillates between both

- Bow steering, the shape of the bow produces forces which cause the boat to sheer to one side. This is often accompanied by a violent roll

- Bow diving, in following seas the bow digs into the wave ahead, resulting in a rapid deceleration, and sometimes almost complete submergence.

- Fast tight turns produce high centrifugal forces which may cause the boat to heel outwards. Particularly applies to round bilge monohulls.

- Stability reduction at speed, making the boat less stable and more difficult to steer.

Look for and know:

- that power trim or trim tabs are adjusted to give the correct running trim
- about guidance on handling as detailed in owner's manual

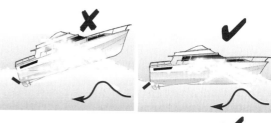

DO:

✔ get proper tuition in handling at speed

✔ read the waves, and use the throttle accordingly

✔ slow right down in busy or restricted waters or if people have to go on deck

✔ use trim controls according to whether it is a head or following sea

DON'T:

✗ make needlessly sharp turns

✗ go too fast for the sea conditions

Inflatables and RIBs

Also see the section on high speed power boats if appropriate

Principal hazards are:

- Swamping as a result of going too fast in waves leading to possible sinking
- Capsizing as a result of bad load distribution, including passengers, causing excessive heel
- Flipping, bow over stern, through driving too hard into a head sea, wash or wind

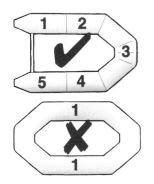

Look for and know:
- the maximum number of people for which the boat is suitable
- the maximum recommended engine power as given in the owner's manual

DESIGN CAT C
MAX 4 PERSONS

- the compartmentation of the inflatable tubes so that if one compartment is punctured the swamped boat will still float reasonably level
- self-bailers in the transom

DO:

✔ keep the tubes firmly inflated

✔ take care to load the boat properly, keeping some weight forward to counterbalance the engine and helmsman

✔ carry less load when it is rough

✔ have an appropriate size pump or bailer attached by a lanyard

✔ check the inflated tubes and bottom compartments in case they have taken on water

DON'T:

✗ overload the boat

✗ go out in conditions inappropriate for the design of boat

✗ go too fast astern, or astern into waves

Personal watercraft

Most personal water craft will capsize, it's part of the fun. What is important is that they can be recovered without damage.

Principal hazards are:
- Capsizing due to waves or bad weight distribution

- Sinking as a result of opening up the engine compartment while afloat

Look for and know:
- the maximum number of people for which the craft is suitable
- which way to roll the craft when recovering after a capsize (to avoid possible engine damage)

DO:
✔ check the flotation, in case the craft has taken on water
✔ know which way to roll the craft when recovering after a capsize

DON'T:
✗ overload the craft
✗ go out in conditions inappropriate for the design of craft
✗ open the engine compartment at sea

Inland waterways boats

This section should be considered in addition to the appropriate section on the specific boat type

Principal hazards are:

• Immersion of openings at large heel angles, leading to loose water inside the boat

• Getting 'hung up' on lock walls or sills

• Capsize due to bad load distribution or over-loading

• Swamping as a result of wash from other boats, or bad positioning when a lock is being filled

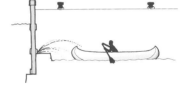

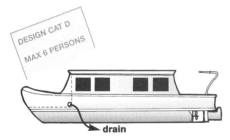

Look for and know:

• that wells and cockpits drain overboard and not into the bilges
• that topside openings are high enough with respect to possible heel and trim angles
• the maximum number of people for which the boat is suitable

DO:
✔ keep the boat at a reasonable heel and trim by positioning the crew
✔ check for water inside the boat and pump out if necessary
✔ open lock paddles gently

DON'T:
✗ overload the craft
✗ tie off your warps when descending in a lock
✗ moor too close to the upper set of lock gates
✗ get too close to weir streams

Annex A - More about stability

A boat is said to be stable when it has an inherent tendency to return to the original upright attitude after some influence has displaced it.

After being completely inverted, only a few boats are so stable that they will return to the upright without help. The extent to which they are positively stable is called the **RANGE OF POSITIVE STABILITY.**

The angle of heel beyond which (in calm water) a boat will invert rather than recover to the upright is called the **ANGLE OF VANISHING STABILITY.**

A boat is stable because the relative positions of the Centre of Gravity (CG) and the Centre of Buoyancy (CB), together with the weight of the boat, create a moment (force x distance) which returns the boat to the upright. The shortest distance between the line of the buoyancy force and that of the weight is called the **RIGHTING LEVER (GZ).**

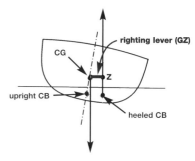

GZ (boat weight) = RM

This lever multiplied by the boat's weight becomes the **RIGHTING MOMENT (RM).**

If the Centre of Gravity (CG) is raised the stability will be reduced and if the CG is lowered the stability is increased. So weight added high up is potentially dangerous.

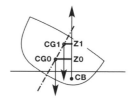

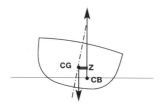

At small angles of heel, the stability is strongly affected by the shape of the part of the hull that is normally underwater (form stable).

At larger angles of heel, the stability is strongly affected by the height of the topsides, the size of the superstructure and the volume of cockpit.

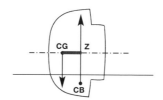

The true position of the CG of a boat is found by conducting an **INCLINING EXPERIMENT** in which known weights are moved through known distances to apply a known heeling moment. By measuring the resulting angle of heel very accurately, and knowing the true weight of the boat, the position of the CG can be determined provided that the shape of the hull is known. Getting an accurate answer requires great care.

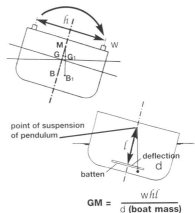

$$GM = \frac{w\,h\,\ell}{d\ (\textbf{boat mass})}$$

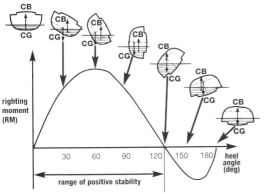

Using a known position of the CG and a computer, it is possible to calculate the stability righting moment at any angle of heel. It is plotted as a graph of righting moment against heel angle. This is called the **RIGHTING MOMENT CURVE.**

For undecked boats where swamping is possible, the Righting Moment Curve has no meaning beyond the angle at which swamping starts.

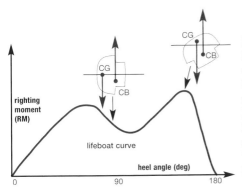

For most motor boats, the part of the Righting Moment Curve up to about 40° heel is the most important. However motor boats intended for very rough weather (like RNLI lifeboats) can be designed to be self-righting, by having very strong, watertight superstructures, so that the Righting Moment is positive at all angles of heel.

For monohull sailing yachts in coastal waters (Design Category C), it is very desirable that the boat should recover from a knockdown. To do this, the Angle of Vanishing Stability must exceed about 100°.

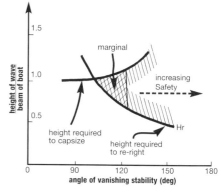

Monohull offshore sailing yachts (Design Categories A and B) risk being struck by very powerful breaking waves. For such boats a large Angle of Vanishing Stability is required. Boats hit by a breaking wave with a height greater than the beam of the yacht are liable to be COMPLETELY INVERTED.

The time taken to recover from an inversion is least when the Angle of Vanishing Stability is closest to 180°, because then only a comparatively small amount of wave energy is needed to start the righting process.

Another measure of the readiness to right after inversion is the ratio between the positive area and the negative area under the righting moment curve.

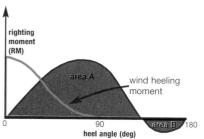

The smaller area B, the better the re-righting

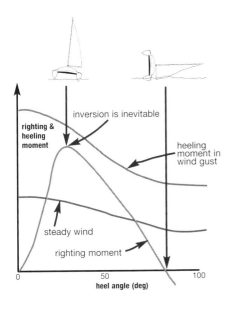

Multihull sailing yachts have very different stability characteristics from most monohulls, because:

- the initial stability is much higher, so that the boat sails almost upright
- the righting moment reaches a maximum at only 10° to 15° heel
- the Angle of Vanishing Stability is often less than 90°
- the wind heeling moment does not decrease to very little at 90° heel

Once the boat is heeled past the angle of maximum righting moment, complete inversion is virtually inevitable, and this will happen very quickly.

The safety of these craft is based on two principles:

1. providing information about which sails should be used in what wind strength and other guidance to help the user minimise the risk of inversion

2. ensuring that if a multihull does invert:
   (a) the boat has sufficient flotation to ensure it does not sink, and
   (b) there is a means of escape for anyone trapped inside the boat

YACHT 'SEABIRD' SAIL COMBINATION	MAXIMUM SAFE WIND
FULL MAIN & GENOA	LIGHT LOAD — HEAVY LOAD
FULL MAIN & JIB	F3 — F4
REEFED MAIN & JIB	F5 — F5
	F6

Annex B - Maximum safe heel angle to prevent downflooding in gusts

Monohull sailing yachts are vulnerable to downflooding when heeled by a sudden gust of wind. By the application of a wind heeling force curve and the righting curve for a given yacht it is possible to determine a safe heel angle for normal sailing that will avoid downflooding in gusts. On the yacht's righting moment curve (RM curve) (see page 25) draw a vertical line at the downflooding angle or 60° if this is less.

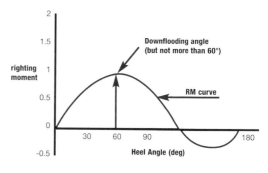

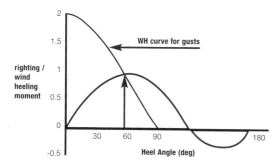

Superimpose a wind heeling curve (WH curve) on the RM curve so that the WH curve crosses the vertical line at its intersection with the RM curve. WH moment varies as $[\cos (\text{heel angle})]^{1.3}$ It is known that in a gust the heeling moment is up to twice that of steady wind. So if we assume that the wind heeling line we have superimposed on the RM curve represents a gust, then a similar WH curve but half the height will represent the steady wind heeling moment.

The right hand end of both WH curves must be 0 at 90°. Draw the WH curve for steady wind from this point back to the left until it crosses the RM curve.

The angle of this intersection will represent a safe angle of heel. Keep to or below this and, even in a gust (though not a squall) the yacht should never reach the downflooding angle.

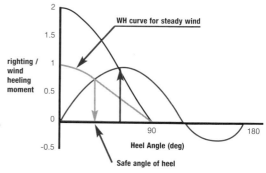

Annex C - Glossary of terms

Weight	The weight of an object, in kilograms or tonnes.
Buoyancy	The upwards force produced when a body is partially or completely immersed in water.
Ballast ratio	The ratio of the fixed ballast mass to the total mass of the boat expressed as a percentage
Flotation	Means of providing buoyancy in a boat after swamping or flooding, e.g. by means of air tanks, air bags or foam material.
Capsize	When a boat is heeled to any angle from which it cannot recover without assistance.
Displacement	The weight of water displaced by a floating object
Knockdown	When a sailing boat is heeled until the masthead enters the water,
Inversion	When a boat turns completely upside down.
Swamping	When a boat is rapidly filled with water from above, eg: by waves.
Flooding	When a boat slowly fills with water, eg: through submerged downflooding openings, or through leaks of fittings below the waterline.
Downflooding	Flooding through openings that are normally above the calm water level.
Design Category	One of four categories defined in the Recreational Craft Directive.
Significant Wave Height	The mean height of the highest one third of waves, as measured at any fixed point in a wave system, measured from crest to trough.
Centre of Gravity (CG)	Effective centre of the weight of all the elements comprising a loaded boat, including hull, ballast, masts, engine(s), crew and stores.
Centre of Buoyancy (CB)	Geometric centre of that part of the hull of a boat that is below the waterline at any instant.
Righting Lever (GZ)	The distance in the horizontal plane between the lines of action of the craft weight and buoyancy.
Righting Moment (RM)	The moment tending to return a boat to the upright, which is the product of the Righting Lever and the Weight of the boat.
Angle of Vanishing Stability (AVS)	The angle of heel at which, in calm water, a boat continues to an inversion rather than returning to the upright.

Annex D - Further reading

Stability Guidance Booklet for Small
Commercial Sailing/Motor Vessels   **MCA**

Teach Yourself Naval Architecture   **B.Baxter**   **Warsash Nautical Bookshop**

Seaworthiness - The Forgotten Factor   **C.A.Marchaj**   **Adlard Coles Ltd**

Principles of Yacht Design   **L.Larsson & R.Eliasson** **Adlard Coles Ltd**

ISO 12217 - Small Craft - Stability
and Buoyancy Assessment and
Categorization   **ISO**

Notes

Notes

RYA Membership

Promoting and Protecting Boating
www.rya.org.uk

RYA Membership

Promoting and Protecting Boating

The RYA is the national organisation which represents the interests of everyone who goes boating for pleasure.

The greater the membership, the louder our voice when it comes to protecting members' interests.

Apply for membership today, and support the RYA, to help the RYA support you.

Benefits of Membership

- Access to expert advice on all aspects of boating from legal wrangles to training matters
- Special members' discounts on a range of products and services including boat insurance, books, videos and class certificates
- Free issue of certificates of competence, increasingly asked for by everyone from overseas governments to holiday companies, insurance underwriters to boat hirers

- Access to the wide range of RYA publications, including the quarterly magazine
- Third Party insurance for windsurfing members
- Free Internet access with RYA-Online
- Special discounts on AA membership
- Regular offers in RYA Magazine
- ...and much more

Join now - membership form opposite

Join online at www.rya.org.uk

Visit our website for information, advice, members' services and web shop.